THIS GARDENING JOURNAL BELONGS TO

_____

_____

_____

CONTACT DETAILS

_____

_____

_____

_____

DEDICATION

This Garden Journal is dedicated to all the gardeners out there who want to track their gardening and document their findings in the process.

You are my inspiration for producing books and I'm honored to be a part of keeping all of your Gardening notes and records organized.

This journal notebook will help you record your details about tracking your garden projects.

Thoughtfully put together with these sections to record: Monthly Harvest Calendar, Projects, Budget, Planting & Sowing PTracker, Seedlings, Weekly To-Do, Pest Control, Garden Organizer, Planner With Grid, & much more!

HOW TO USE THIS BOOK

The purpose of this book is to keep all of your Garden notes all in one place. It will help keep you organized.

This Garden Journal will allow you to accurately document every detail about your garden projects. It's a great way to chart your course through tracking your gardening experience.

Here are examples of the prompts for you to fill in and write about your experience in this book:

1. Monthly Harvest Calendar - Undated to keep track of harvest through the gardening season.
2. Gardening Projects - Record your goals for new projects, including techniques.
3. Produce Budget - Plan for your fruit/ vegetable budget shopping.
4. Planting Tracker - Track your planting activities.
5. Garden Wish List - List those fruits, vegetables, or flowers you would like to grow.
6. Garden Budget - Detailed budget planner data.
7. Seedlings - Log your seedlings information.
8. Weekly To-Do - Record your tasks for the week.
9. Pest Control Record - Log any pests and treatment to rid them.
10. Sowing Tracker - Track your sowing.
11. Seed Inventory Log - Record all the important info about your seeds, vegetable, or flowers.
12. Seed Purchase - Where you bought the seeds, price & quantity.
13. Garden Organizer - Plan where everything will go.
14. Succession Sowing Tracker - Track your succession sowing.
15. Harvest Tracker - Track your harvest, weight, quantity, variety & value.
16. Crop Rotation Log - Log where your crop will be planted for the following season.
17. Growing Notes - Important information you need to write.
18. Seed Packet Info Tracker - Record variety, sowing depth, days to germinate, days to maturity & harvest window.
19. Planner (Square Foot) - Grid to sketch out your garden plans.
20. Gardening Expense Tracker - Items, description, qty, price, notes, total expense.
21. Plant List - Track most important crops, crops to preserve & fast-growing crops.
22. Gardening To-Do List - Blank lined to record tasks & notes.
23. Seasonal To-Do List - To-Do List for spring, summer, winter, fall.
24. Gardening Page Notes - Any important information you need to record and know or ideas you need for the following year to look back on.

SUPPLIER CONTACT LIST

COMPANY	STREET	PRODUCTS
WEBSITE	CITY	
EMAIL	STATE	
CONTACT	ZIP CODE	

COMPANY	STREET	PRODUCTS
WEBSITE	CITY	
EMAIL	STATE	
CONTACT	ZIP CODE	

COMPANY	STREET	PRODUCTS
WEBSITE	CITY	
EMAIL	STATE	
CONTACT	ZIP CODE	

COMPANY	STREET	PRODUCTS
WEBSITE	CITY	
EMAIL	STATE	
CONTACT	ZIP CODE	

COMPANY	STREET	PRODUCTS
WEBSITE	CITY	
EMAIL	STATE	
CONTACT	ZIP CODE	

COMPANY	STREET	PRODUCTS
WEBSITE	CITY	
EMAIL	STATE	
CONTACT	ZIP CODE	

SUPPLIER CONTACT LIST

COMPANY	STREET	PRODUCTS
WEBSITE	CITY	
EMAIL	STATE	
CONTACT	ZIP CODE	

COMPANY	STREET	PRODUCTS
WEBSITE	CITY	
EMAIL	STATE	
CONTACT	ZIP CODE	

COMPANY	STREET	PRODUCTS
WEBSITE	CITY	
EMAIL	STATE	
CONTACT	ZIP CODE	

COMPANY	STREET	PRODUCTS
WEBSITE	CITY	
EMAIL	STATE	
CONTACT	ZIP CODE	

COMPANY	STREET	PRODUCTS
WEBSITE	CITY	
EMAIL	STATE	
CONTACT	ZIP CODE	

COMPANY	STREET	PRODUCTS
WEBSITE	CITY	
EMAIL	STATE	
CONTACT	ZIP CODE	

SUPPLIER CONTACT LIST

COMPANY	STREET	PRODUCTS
WEBSITE	CITY	
EMAIL	STATE	
CONTACT	ZIP CODE	

COMPANY	STREET	PRODUCTS
WEBSITE	CITY	
EMAIL	STATE	
CONTACT	ZIP CODE	

COMPANY	STREET	PRODUCTS
WEBSITE	CITY	
EMAIL	STATE	
CONTACT	ZIP CODE	

COMPANY	STREET	PRODUCTS
WEBSITE	CITY	
EMAIL	STATE	
CONTACT	ZIP CODE	

COMPANY	STREET	PRODUCTS
WEBSITE	CITY	
EMAIL	STATE	
CONTACT	ZIP CODE	

COMPANY	STREET	PRODUCTS
WEBSITE	CITY	
EMAIL	STATE	
CONTACT	ZIP CODE	

SUPPLIER CONTACT LIST

COMPANY	STREET	PRODUCTS
WEBSITE	CITY	
EMAIL	STATE	
CONTACT	ZIP CODE	

COMPANY	STREET	PRODUCTS
WEBSITE	CITY	
EMAIL	STATE	
CONTACT	ZIP CODE	

COMPANY	STREET	PRODUCTS
WEBSITE	CITY	
EMAIL	STATE	
CONTACT	ZIP CODE	

COMPANY	STREET	PRODUCTS
WEBSITE	CITY	
EMAIL	STATE	
CONTACT	ZIP CODE	

COMPANY	STREET	PRODUCTS
WEBSITE	CITY	
EMAIL	STATE	
CONTACT	ZIP CODE	

COMPANY	STREET	PRODUCTS
WEBSITE	CITY	
EMAIL	STATE	
CONTACT	ZIP CODE	

SUPPLIER CONTACT LIST

COMPANY	STREET	PRODUCTS
WEBSITE	CITY	
EMAIL	STATE	
CONTACT	ZIP CODE	

COMPANY	STREET	PRODUCTS
WEBSITE	CITY	
EMAIL	STATE	
CONTACT	ZIP CODE	

COMPANY	STREET	PRODUCTS
WEBSITE	CITY	
EMAIL	STATE	
CONTACT	ZIP CODE	

COMPANY	STREET	PRODUCTS
WEBSITE	CITY	
EMAIL	STATE	
CONTACT	ZIP CODE	

COMPANY	STREET	PRODUCTS
WEBSITE	CITY	
EMAIL	STATE	
CONTACT	ZIP CODE	

COMPANY	STREET	PRODUCTS
WEBSITE	CITY	
EMAIL	STATE	
CONTACT	ZIP CODE	

WEATHER LOG

DATE	CODE	TEMPERATURE	HUMIDITY

WEATHER LOG

DATE	CODE	TEMPERATURE	HUMIDITY

WEATHER LOG

DATE	CODE	TEMPERATURE	HUMIDITY

WEATHER LOG

DATE	CODE	TEMPERATURE	HUMIDITY

WEATHER LOG

DATE	CODE	TEMPERATURE	HUMIDITY

WEATHER LOG

DATE	CODE	TEMPERATURE	HUMIDITY

WEATHER LOG

DATE	CODE	TEMPERATURE	HUMIDITY

WEATHER LOG

DATE	CODE	TEMPERATURE	HUMIDITY

WEATHER LOG

DATE	CODE	TEMPERATURE	HUMIDITY

WEATHER LOG

DATE	CODE	TEMPERATURE	HUMIDITY

GARDEN PLOTTING NOTES

_____

_____

_____

_____

_____

_____

_____

_____

_____

_____

_____

_____

_____

_____

_____

_____

_____

_____

GARDEN PLOTTING NOTES

GARDEN PLOTTING NOTES

_____

_____

_____

_____

_____

_____

_____

_____

_____

_____

_____

_____

_____

_____

_____

_____

_____

_____

GARDEN PLOTTING PLAN

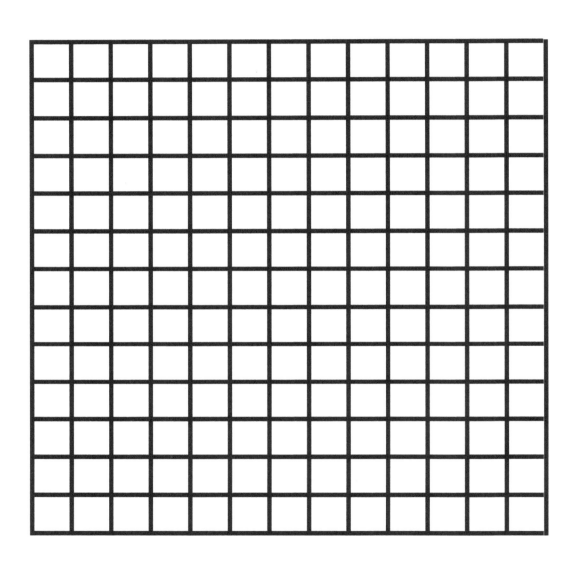

GARDEN PLOTTING PLAN

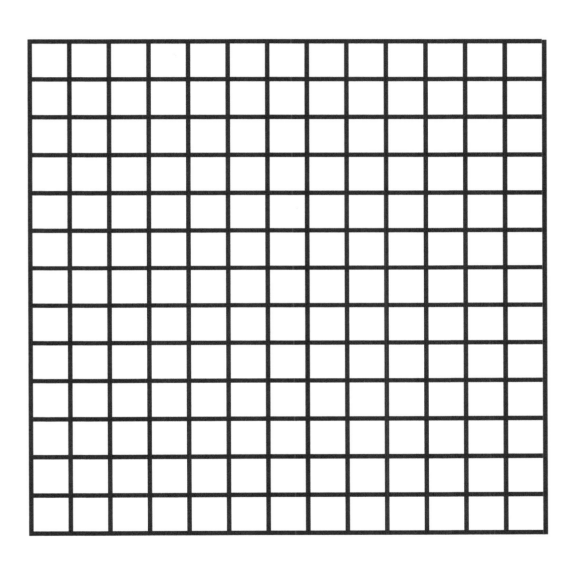

WHEN TO PLANT CHECKLIST

PLANT NAME	J	F	M	A	M	J	J	A	S	O	N	D

WHEN TO PLANT CHECKLIST

PLANT NAME	J	F	M	A	M	J	J	A	S	O	N	D

MONTHLY LOG
JANUARY
WEEK 1

PLANTING	PROPAGATION	PRUNING

MAINTENANCE	PEST CONTROL	OTHER

WEATHER	WILDLIFE

BLOOMS	HIGHLIGHTS

PURCHASED	COST	HARVESTING	AMOUNT

MONTHLY LOG
JANUARY
WEEK 2

PLANTING	PROPAGATION	PRUNING

MAINTENANCE	PEST CONTROL	OTHER

WEATHER	WILDLIFE

BLOOMS	HIGHLIGHTS

PURCHASED	COST	HARVESTING	AMOUNT

MONTHLY LOG
JANUARY
WEEK 3

PLANTING	PROPAGATION	PRUNING

MAINTENANCE	PEST CONTROL	OTHER

WEATHER	WILDLIFE

BLOOMS	HIGHLIGHTS

PURCHASED	COST	HARVESTING	AMOUNT

MONTHLY LOG
JANUARY
WEEK 4

PLANTING	PROPAGATION	PRUNING

MAINTENANCE	PEST CONTROL	OTHER

WEATHER	WILDLIFE

BLOOMS	HIGHLIGHTS

PURCHASED	COST	HARVESTING	AMOUNT

MONTHLY LOG
JANUARY
WEEK 5

PLANTING	PROPAGATION	PRUNING

MAINTENANCE	PEST CONTROL	OTHER

WEATHER	WILDLIFE

BLOOMS	HIGHLIGHTS

PURCHASED	COST	HARVESTING	AMOUNT

MONTHLY LOG
FEBRUARY
WEEK 1

PLANTING	PROPAGATION	PRUNING

MAINTENANCE	PEST CONTROL	OTHER

WEATHER	WILDLIFE

BLOOMS	HIGHLIGHTS

PURCHASED	COST	HARVESTING	AMOUNT

MONTHLY LOG
FEBRUARY
WEEK 2

PLANTING	PROPAGATION	PRUNING

MAINTENANCE	PEST CONTROL	OTHER

WEATHER	WILDLIFE

BLOOMS	HIGHLIGHTS

PURCHASED	COST	HARVESTING	AMOUNT

MONTHLY LOG
FEBRUARY
WEEK 3

PLANTING	PROPAGATION	PRUNING

MAINTENANCE	PEST CONTROL	OTHER

WEATHER	WILDLIFE

BLOOMS	HIGHLIGHTS

PURCHASED	COST	HARVESTING	AMOUNT

MONTHLY LOG
FEBRUARY
WEEK 4

PLANTING	PROPAGATION	PRUNING

MAINTENANCE	PEST CONTROL	OTHER

WEATHER	WILDLIFE

BLOOMS	HIGHLIGHTS

PURCHASED	COST	HARVESTING	AMOUNT

MONTHLY LOG
FEBRUARY
WEEK 5

PLANTING	PROPAGATION	PRUNING

MAINTENANCE	PEST CONTROL	OTHER

WEATHER	WILDLIFE

BLOOMS	HIGHLIGHTS

PURCHASED	COST	HARVESTING	AMOUNT

MONTHLY LOG
MARCH
WEEK 1

PLANTING	PROPAGATION	PRUNING

_____
_____
_____
_____
_____

MAINTENANCE	PEST CONTROL	OTHER

_____
_____
_____
_____
_____
_____

WEATHER	WILDLIFE

BLOOMS	HIGHLIGHTS

PURCHASED	COST	HARVESTING	AMOUNT

MONTHLY LOG
MARCH
WEEK 2

PLANTING	PROPAGATION	PRUNING

MAINTENANCE	PEST CONTROL	OTHER

WEATHER	WILDLIFE

BLOOMS	HIGHLIGHTS

PURCHASED	COST	HARVESTING	AMOUNT

MONTHLY LOG
MARCH
WEEK 3

PLANTING	PROPAGATION	PRUNING

MAINTENANCE	PEST CONTROL	OTHER

WEATHER	WILDLIFE

BLOOMS	HIGHLIGHTS

PURCHASED	COST	HARVESTING	AMOUNT

MONTHLY LOG
MARCH
WEEK 4

PLANTING	PROPAGATION	PRUNING

MAINTENANCE	PEST CONTROL	OTHER

WEATHER	WILDLIFE

BLOOMS	HIGHLIGHTS

PURCHASED	COST	HARVESTING	AMOUNT

MONTHLY LOG
MARCH
WEEK 5

PLANTING	PROPAGATION	PRUNING

MAINTENANCE	PEST CONTROL	OTHER

WEATHER	WILDLIFE

BLOOMS	HIGHLIGHTS

PURCHASED	COST	HARVESTING	AMOUNT

MONTHLY LOG
APRIL
WEEK 1

PLANTING	PROPAGATION	PRUNING

MAINTENANCE	PEST CONTROL	OTHER

WEATHER	WILDLIFE

BLOOMS	HIGHLIGHTS

PURCHASED	COST	HARVESTING	AMOUNT

MONTHLY LOG
APRIL
WEEK 2

PLANTING	PROPAGATION	PRUNING

MAINTENANCE	PEST CONTROL	OTHER

WEATHER	WILDLIFE

BLOOMS	HIGHLIGHTS

PURCHASED	COST	HARVESTING	AMOUNT

MONTHLY LOG
APRIL
WEEK 3

PLANTING	PROPAGATION	PRUNING

MAINTENANCE	PEST CONTROL	OTHER

WEATHER	WILDLIFE

BLOOMS	HIGHLIGHTS

PURCHASED	COST	HARVESTING	AMOUNT

MONTHLY LOG
APRIL
WEEK 4

PLANTING	PROPAGATION	PRUNING

MAINTENANCE	PEST CONTROL	OTHER

WEATHER	WILDLIFE

BLOOMS	HIGHLIGHTS

PURCHASED	COST	HARVESTING	AMOUNT

MONTHLY LOG
APRIL
WEEK 5

PLANTING	PROPAGATION	PRUNING

MAINTENANCE	PEST CONTROL	OTHER

WEATHER	WILDLIFE

BLOOMS	HIGHLIGHTS

PURCHASED	COST	HARVESTING	AMOUNT

MONTHLY LOG
MAY
WEEK 1

PLANTING	PROPAGATION	PRUNING

MAINTENANCE	PEST CONTROL	OTHER

WEATHER	WILDLIFE

BLOOMS	HIGHLIGHTS

PURCHASED	COST	HARVESTING	AMOUNT

MONTHLY LOG
MAY
WEEK 2

PLANTING	PROPAGATION	PRUNING

MAINTENANCE	PEST CONTROL	OTHER

WEATHER	WILDLIFE

BLOOMS	HIGHLIGHTS

PURCHASED	COST	HARVESTING	AMOUNT

MONTHLY LOG
MAY
WEEK 3

PLANTING	PROPAGATION	PRUNING

MAINTENANCE	PEST CONTROL	OTHER

WEATHER	WILDLIFE

BLOOMS	HIGHLIGHTS

PURCHASED	COST	HARVESTING	AMOUNT

MONTHLY LOG
MAY
WEEK 4

PLANTING	PROPAGATION	PRUNING

MAINTENANCE	PEST CONTROL	OTHER

WEATHER	WILDLIFE

BLOOMS	HIGHLIGHTS

PURCHASED	COST	HARVESTING	AMOUNT

MONTHLY LOG
MAY
WEEK 5

PLANTING	PROPAGATION	PRUNING

MAINTENANCE	PEST CONTROL	OTHER

WEATHER	WILDLIFE

BLOOMS	HIGHLIGHTS

PURCHASED	COST	HARVESTING	AMOUNT

MONTHLY LOG
JUNE
WEEK 1

PLANTING	PROPAGATION	PRUNING

MAINTENANCE	PEST CONTROL	OTHER

WEATHER	WILDLIFE

BLOOMS	HIGHLIGHTS

PURCHASED	COST	HARVESTING	AMOUNT

MONTHLY LOG
JUNE
WEEK 2

PLANTING	PROPAGATION	PRUNING

MAINTENANCE	PEST CONTROL	OTHER

WEATHER	WILDLIFE

BLOOMS	HIGHLIGHTS

PURCHASED	COST	HARVESTING	AMOUNT

MONTHLY LOG
JUNE
WEEK 3

PLANTING	PROPAGATION	PRUNING

MAINTENANCE	PEST CONTROL	OTHER

WEATHER	WILDLIFE

BLOOMS	HIGHLIGHTS

PURCHASED	COST	HARVESTING	AMOUNT

MONTHLY LOG
JUNE
WEEK 4

PLANTING	PROPAGATION	PRUNING

MAINTENANCE	PEST CONTROL	OTHER

WEATHER	WILDLIFE

BLOOMS	HIGHLIGHTS

PURCHASED	COST	HARVESTING	AMOUNT

MONTHLY LOG
JUNE
WEEK 5

PLANTING	PROPAGATION	PRUNING

MAINTENANCE	PEST CONTROL	OTHER

WEATHER	WILDLIFE

BLOOMS	HIGHLIGHTS

PURCHASED	COST	HARVESTING	AMOUNT

MONTHLY LOG
JULY
WEEK 1

PLANTING	PROPAGATION	PRUNING

MAINTENANCE	PEST CONTROL	OTHER

WEATHER	WILDLIFE

BLOOMS	HIGHLIGHTS

PURCHASED	COST	HARVESTING	AMOUNT

MONTHLY LOG
JULY
WEEK 2

PLANTING	PROPAGATION	PRUNING

MAINTENANCE	PEST CONTROL	OTHER

WEATHER	WILDLIFE

BLOOMS	HIGHLIGHTS

PURCHASED	COST	HARVESTING	AMOUNT

MONTHLY LOG
JULY
WEEK 3

PLANTING	PROPAGATION	PRUNING

MAINTENANCE	PEST CONTROL	OTHER

WEATHER	WILDLIFE

BLOOMS	HIGHLIGHTS

PURCHASED	COST	HARVESTING	AMOUNT

MONTHLY LOG
JULY
WEEK 4

PLANTING	PROPAGATION	PRUNING

MAINTENANCE	PEST CONTROL	OTHER

WEATHER	WILDLIFE

BLOOMS	HIGHLIGHTS

PURCHASED	COST	HARVESTING	AMOUNT

MONTHLY LOG
JULY
WEEK 5

PLANTING	PROPAGATION	PRUNING

MAINTENANCE	PEST CONTROL	OTHER

WEATHER	WILDLIFE

BLOOMS	HIGHLIGHTS

PURCHASED	COST	HARVESTING	AMOUNT

MONTHLY LOG
AUGUST
WEEK 1

PLANTING	PROPAGATION	PRUNING

MAINTENANCE	PEST CONTROL	OTHER

WEATHER	WILDLIFE

BLOOMS	HIGHLIGHTS

PURCHASED	COST	HARVESTING	AMOUNT

MONTHLY LOG
AUGUST
WEEK 2

PLANTING	PROPAGATION	PRUNING

MAINTENANCE	PEST CONTROL	OTHER

WEATHER	WILDLIFE

BLOOMS	HIGHLIGHTS

PURCHASED	COST	HARVESTING	AMOUNT

MONTHLY LOG
AUGUST
WEEK 3

PLANTING	PROPAGATION	PRUNING

MAINTENANCE	PEST CONTROL	OTHER

WEATHER	WILDLIFE

BLOOMS	HIGHLIGHTS

PURCHASED	COST	HARVESTING	AMOUNT

MONTHLY LOG
AUGUST
WEEK 4

PLANTING	PROPAGATION	PRUNING

MAINTENANCE	PEST CONTROL	OTHER

WEATHER	WILDLIFE

BLOOMS	HIGHLIGHTS

PURCHASED	COST	HARVESTING	AMOUNT

MONTHLY LOG
AUGUST
WEEK 5

PLANTING	PROPAGATION	PRUNING

MAINTENANCE	PEST CONTROL	OTHER

WEATHER	WILDLIFE

BLOOMS	HIGHLIGHTS

PURCHASED	COST	HARVESTING	AMOUNT

MONTHLY LOG
SEPTEMBER
WEEK 1

PLANTING   PROPAGATION   PRUNING

MAINTENANCE   PEST CONTROL   OTHER

WEATHER	WILDLIFE

BLOOMS	HIGHLIGHTS

PURCHASED	COST	HARVESTING	AMOUNT

MONTHLY LOG
SEPTEMBER
WEEK 2

PLANTING	PROPAGATION	PRUNING

MAINTENANCE	PEST CONTROL	OTHER

WEATHER	WILDLIFE

BLOOMS	HIGHLIGHTS

PURCHASED	COST	HARVESTING	AMOUNT

MONTHLY LOG
SEPTEMBER
WEEK 3

PLANTING	PROPAGATION	PRUNING

MAINTENANCE	PEST CONTROL	OTHER

WEATHER	WILDLIFE

BLOOMS	HIGHLIGHTS

PURCHASED	COST	HARVESTING	AMOUNT

MONTHLY LOG
SEPTEMBER
WEEK 4

PLANTING	PROPAGATION	PRUNING

MAINTENANCE	PEST CONTROL	OTHER

WEATHER	WILDLIFE

BLOOMS	HIGHLIGHTS

PURCHASED	COST	HARVESTING	AMOUNT

MONTHLY LOG
SEPTEMBER
WEEK 5

PLANTING	PROPAGATION	PRUNING

MAINTENANCE	PEST CONTROL	OTHER

WEATHER	WILDLIFE

BLOOMS	HIGHLIGHTS

PURCHASED	COST	HARVESTING	AMOUNT

MONTHLY LOG
OCTOBER
WEEK 1

PLANTING	PROPAGATION	PRUNING

MAINTENANCE	PEST CONTROL	OTHER

WEATHER	WILDLIFE

BLOOMS	HIGHLIGHTS

PURCHASED	COST	HARVESTING	AMOUNT

MONTHLY LOG
OCTOBER
WEEK 2

PLANTING	PROPAGATION	PRUNING

MAINTENANCE	PEST CONTROL	OTHER

WEATHER	WILDLIFE

BLOOMS	HIGHLIGHTS

PURCHASED	COST	HARVESTING	AMOUNT

MONTHLY LOG
OCTOBER
WEEK 3

PLANTING	PROPAGATION	PRUNING

MAINTENANCE	PEST CONTROL	OTHER

WEATHER	WILDLIFE

BLOOMS	HIGHLIGHTS

PURCHASED	COST	HARVESTING	AMOUNT

MONTHLY LOG
OCTOBER
WEEK 4

PLANTING	PROPAGATION	PRUNING

MAINTENANCE	PEST CONTROL	OTHER

WEATHER	WILDLIFE

BLOOMS	HIGHLIGHTS

PURCHASED	COST	HARVESTING	AMOUNT

MONTHLY LOG
OCTOBER
WEEK 5

PLANTING	PROPAGATION	PRUNING

MAINTENANCE	PEST CONTROL	OTHER

WEATHER	WILDLIFE

BLOOMS	HIGHLIGHTS

PURCHASED	COST	HARVESTING	AMOUNT

MONTHLY LOG
NOVEMBER
WEEK 1

PLANTING	PROPAGATION	PRUNING

MAINTENANCE	PEST CONTROL	OTHER

WEATHER	WILDLIFE

BLOOMS	HIGHLIGHTS

PURCHASED	COST	HARVESTING	AMOUNT

MONTHLY LOG
NOVEMBER
WEEK 2

PLANTING	PROPAGATION	PRUNING

MAINTENANCE	PEST CONTROL	OTHER

WEATHER	WILDLIFE

BLOOMS	HIGHLIGHTS

PURCHASED	COST	HARVESTING	AMOUNT

MONTHLY LOG
NOVEMBER
WEEK 3

PLANTING	PROPAGATION	PRUNING

MAINTENANCE	PEST CONTROL	OTHER

WEATHER	WILDLIFE

BLOOMS	HIGHLIGHTS

PURCHASED	COST	HARVESTING	AMOUNT

MONTHLY LOG
NOVEMBER
WEEK 4

PLANTING	PROPAGATION	PRUNING

MAINTENANCE	PEST CONTROL	OTHER

WEATHER	WILDLIFE

BLOOMS	HIGHLIGHTS

PURCHASED	COST	HARVESTING	AMOUNT

MONTHLY LOG
NOVEMBER
WEEK 5

PLANTING	PROPAGATION	PRUNING

MAINTENANCE	PEST CONTROL	OTHER

WEATHER	WILDLIFE

BLOOMS	HIGHLIGHTS

PURCHASED	COST	HARVESTING	AMOUNT

MONTHLY LOG
DECEMBER
WEEK 1

PLANTING	PROPAGATION	PRUNING

MAINTENANCE	PEST CONTROL	OTHER

WEATHER	WILDLIFE

BLOOMS	HIGHLIGHTS

PURCHASED	COST	HARVESTING	AMOUNT

MONTHLY LOG
DECEMBER
WEEK 2

PLANTING	PROPAGATION	PRUNING

MAINTENANCE	PEST CONTROL	OTHER

WEATHER	WILDLIFE

BLOOMS	HIGHLIGHTS

PURCHASED	COST	HARVESTING	AMOUNT

MONTHLY LOG
DECEMBER
WEEK 3

PLANTING	PROPAGATION	PRUNING

MAINTENANCE	PEST CONTROL	OTHER

WEATHER	WILDLIFE

BLOOMS	HIGHLIGHTS

PURCHASED	COST	HARVESTING	AMOUNT

MONTHLY LOG
DECEMBER
WEEK 4

PLANTING	PROPAGATION	PRUNING

MAINTENANCE	PEST CONTROL	OTHER

WEATHER	WILDLIFE

BLOOMS	HIGHLIGHTS

PURCHASED	COST	HARVESTING	AMOUNT

MONTHLY LOG
DECEMBER
WEEK 5

PLANTING	PROPAGATION	PRUNING

MAINTENANCE	PEST CONTROL	OTHER

WEATHER	WILDLIFE

BLOOMS	HIGHLIGHTS

PURCHASED	COST	HARVESTING	AMOUNT

CPSIA information can be obtained
at www.ICGtesting.com
Printed in the USA
LVHW100811100121
676043LV00011B/646